# Whiz Macgael

Tales of a talented dog

Delightful keepsake book of doggy tales.

.........................................................................

.........................................................................

# The Heroic Escapades of Whiz Macgael

The Heroic Escapades of Whiz Macgael

Les escapades héroïques de Whiz Macgael

Na réimeanna cróga ó Whiz Macgael

Author and photographer: **U McRory**

Illustrator: **C Hamill**

Vet

Fire

Water

# The Heroic Escapades of Whiz Macgael

First edition published in 2019 by Grá Ultana Ltd., Ireland

Copyright © 2019 U. M. McRory

Photographs, stories, text, illustrations, interior design including book cover all copyright © 2019 U. M. McRory

Printed in Andika New Basic 14 point, 64 pages

Illustrations by Caroline Hamill

Edited by Louise McMullan

Irish checked by Aoife Mhic Niocóil and Cathal Ó Manacháin

French checked by Régine McCullough

Book cover and interior design by U. M. McRory and Caroline Hamill

ISBN 978-0-9556649-1-5 (hardback)

Website: whizmacgael.ie

Interest Level: Age 7+      Genre: Children's fiction animal story

Language: English (UK and Ireland) with selected words translated into French and Irish

Grá Ultana Ltd uses paper from sustainable sources

Printed in Ireland by W&G Baird

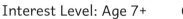

FSC
www.fsc.org
MIX
Paper from
responsible sources
FSC® C016201

# Contents

# Meet Whiz Macgael

Looking after me

Affectionate
Brave
Charming
Dog

Begin to learn the French and Irish languages

| English | | |
|---|---|---|
| English | Welcome. | dog |
| Français (French) | Bienvenue. | chienne |
| Gaeilge (Irish) | Fáilte. | madra |

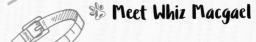
## Meet Whiz Macgael

**Hello.**

I am a very special, talented, unique dog and that is why my observant owner, Ultana, calls me 'Whiz Macgael'.

Hello.
Bonjour.
Dia duit.

I am a dog.
Je suis une chienne.
Is madra mé.

My name is Whiz Macgael.
Je m'appelle Whiz Macgael.
Is mise Whiz Macgael.

My coat is a beautiful golden colour and velvety soft to touch. On my last birthday, I was eight years old.

**8**

I am eight years old.
J'ai huit ans.
Tá mé ocht mbliana d'aois.

I consider myself exceptionally brave and friendly with kind, gentle, brown eyes. Ultana carefully cares for me by bathing, brushing, feeding and keeping me fit.

brown

marron

donn

As a placid, small dog, I love posing for photographs taken in different places by Ultana who also acts as my photographer.

Photographs:
Look cute and pretty
**Pose**

Each morning, I eagerly await my daily feed of nutritious dog nuts served in a brown dish and local well water presented in a blue one.

**Scrumptious**

food

nourriture

bia

water

eau

uisce

I eat dog food and drink water.

Je mange de la nourriture pour chiens et je bois de l'eau.

Ithim bia madraí agus ólaim uisce.

Ultana has given me different foods to taste and now knows my likes and dislikes very well. I have a love for variety and trying new foods. Chewing on dental dog treats as well as munching and gnawing on raw food pieces are enjoyable pastimes.

My home, located in a wooden kennel, is behind Ultana's two-storey house in the spacious back garden.

**Home Sweet Home**

My address is:

Mon adresse est :

Mo sheoladh:

'The Kennel
The Back Garden'

kennel
niche
cró madra

garden
jardin
gairdín

I live in a dog kennel in the garden.

J'habite dans une niche dans le jardin.

Tá mé i mo chónaí i gcró madra sa ghairdín.

9

I love to walk in the countryside with Ultana. She usually carries a small biodegradable and compostable bag and tries to ignore the whiff when lifting my poo. At home, I occupy myself by resting in my kennel, helping with animals on the farm next to the house, or playing, walking and running in the garden.

**Daily Exercise**

I exercise daily.

Je fais de l'exercice tous les jours.

Déanaim aclaíocht gach lá.

My paws are small and, surprisingly, my body too light in weight to bounce on the trampoline in the garden.

paws

pattes

lapaí

trampoline

trampoline

trampailín

Besides, the slide is too slippery for my little paws. When children visit, I enjoy watching them glide down the slide, bounce high on the trampoline and sway happily on the swing.

slide

toboggan

sleamhnán

It is important to realise that it would not be sensible to leave the lawn by myself because of speeding cars and my eyesight. In brief, I am nearsighted and slightly colour blind so only see specific colours. Although I know my Green Cross Code, Ultana takes me across the road for safety.

Finian is a farm owner. Not only do I assist him to transfer cattle from one green field to another, but normally my barking helps make them move faster. However, some days I encounter a cow that chases after me!

cow
vache
bó

shed
hangar
seid

When I peer out the front door of my kennel, the farm shed faces me from the opposite side of the garden. As daylight fades towards the darkness of dusk, I withdraw to the warmer farm shed for better protection from the wind and rain.

At night, I usually sleep soundly in my doggy bed, although on some nights I snooze, getting only forty winks. My dreamy slumber is sometimes disrupted by cattle mooing or sheep bleating in the fields, by a bird pecking at the window or a mouse scampering around inside the shed.

After awakening with the early morning sunrise, I jump up onto straw bales and give a few loud barks at the window. With wagging tail, I wait with anticipation for the opening of the door and love when Ultana strokes my head and gives me, 'her darling pet', my freedom.

tail

queue

eireaball

I bark and wag my tail.

J'aboie et je remue la queue.

Bím ag tafann agus croithim m'eireaball.

Read about my three entertaining escapades, without delay, in the following adventure stories.

Love,

Amitiés,

Le grá,

Whiz Macgael.

# The Fire Adventure

Fire risks and safety

The Fire Adventure
L'aventure du feu
Eachtra an Dóiteáin

Contact the Fire Service to extinguish a fire

13

One beautiful spring morning, after my morning run and breakfast, I was planning my activities for the day while resting on a comfy cushion in my garden kennel. Suddenly, an unfamiliar smell wafted into my nostrils. Hopping up, I raced outside as fast as my four paws could carry me.

four paws
quatre pattes
ceithre lapa

**4**

spring
printemps
an t-earrach

Sniffing around, I followed the odour. Looking up, I saw a greyish-white haze of smoke coming from the shed opposite. Giant flames were leaping from its roof, along with strange crackling sounds. Something must be wrong; I instantly thought to myself. Flames have never jumped up from the shed before. Quickly, I started to bark, yelp, snarl and growl. Feeling frightened, some weird sounds came from my mouth, and I hoped that Ultana would hear me. Almost immediately, she appeared at the door and ran from the house, in her pyjamas, to check why I was making such a hullabaloo.

flames
flammes
lasracha

Relieved, I raced towards her. As soon as she spotted the flames rising upwards from the shed roof, she looked stunned. "Oh no. Fire! Help! I need the Fire Service," Ultana screamed.

Fire!
Au feu !
Tine!

**The flames are scary. I must telephone the emergency services.**

Ultana telephones the emergency services.

Ultana téléphone aux services d'urgence.

Cuireann Ultana fios ar na seirbhísí éigeandála.

Hastily, she sprinted back inside the house, with me scampering behind her to escape from the blaze. Hardly had she grabbed the telephone, and pushed the buttons before someone answered very quickly: "Which service?" the operator asked. In the meantime, I listened as Ultana had the phone on handsfree loudspeaker.

112 – Europe & India
999 – UK & Ireland
000 – Australia
911– Canada & USA
119 – China & Japan
111 – New Zealand

**Fire Service. Please send a fire engine as quickly as possible. The farm shed is on fire.**

The farm shed is on fire.

Le hangar de la ferme est en feu.

Tá an tseid feirme trí thine!

Ultana explained to the operator that the shed was behind the house. She also gave her name, her address and confirmed her telephone number.

After the telephone call had finished, Ultana dressed quickly. Without warning, a loud noise started in the kitchen. "Oh no, the smoke from the shed has set off the smoke alarm," shouted Ultana.

smoke alarm
détecteur de fumée
aláram deataigh

By this stage, I was beginning to feel a little frantic. Never, on any occasion - not once before - had I heard such a noisy din in the kitchen. Pandemonium. Ultana grabbed the fire blanket and fire extinguisher from the wall. I ran outside to get away from the scary noise and stood ready to help at the back door. Quickly closing the door she rushed to the shed but, soon, hurried back to the house.

fire blanket
couverture anti-feu
pluid dóiteáin

Whiz Macgael, the flames are scorching hot and much too high for the fire extinguisher.

fire extinguisher
extincteur
múchtóir dóiteáin

Realising my thirst, Ultana scurried to rescue my food and water from the garden kennel. Lifting me carefully in her arms, she dashed to the garage and placed me inside. As soon as she patted my head and stroked me for a few moments, I felt comforted and not as frightened.

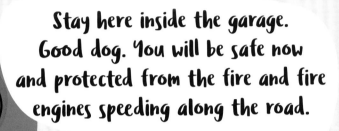

Stay here inside the garage. Good dog. You will be safe now and protected from the fire and fire engines speeding along the road.

Looking out from the garage window, I viewed what was happening. Ultana closed the garage door securely, fearing that I would run to the shed while she stood outside the window.

> burning
> en flammes
> ag dó

Finian noticed the burning building from the farm where he was feeding his cattle. Without delay, he came racing across the field towards the house and yelled, between gasps of breath, for Ultana to telephone the fire service. In contrast, she calmly reassured him that they were on their way.

> Finian runs to the shed.
> Finian court vers le hangar de la ferme.
> Ritheann Finian go dtí an tseid.

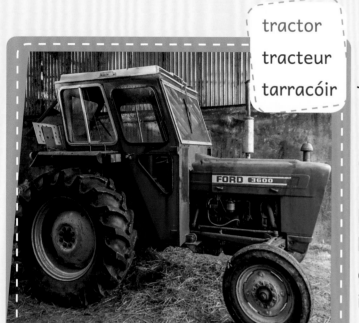

tractor

tracteur

tarracóir

Running into the shed, Finian jumped onto his tractor and started the engine straight away. Lurching forward, he chugged down the road in the big blue machine. After parking, he bounded to the shed again but had to leap back from the glowing flames. In reality, it was impossible to enter. Closing the door, he hastened to the garage window.

"I couldn't rescue any other items as the flames are red-hot," Finian told Ultana.

rescue

secours

tarrtháil

"You were lucky not to be burned or injured, Finian. It is essential to get out and stay out of a burning building. Risking your life to rescue the tractor was not a good idea. It is safer to leave it to the firefighters to put out the fire," replied Ultana.

In the event of a fire:
Get out! Stay out and away from the fire! Call the Fire Service.

En cas d'incendie:
Sortez! Restez dehors et loin de l'incendie! Appelez les pompiers.

I gcás dóiteáin:
Téigh amach! Fan amuigh ón tine! Cuir fios ar an mbriogáid dóiteáin.

# 10

I looked out frequently from the garage window and saw Finian pacing up and down outside. Ultana glanced at her watch. "They should be here soon. I phoned about ten minutes ago," asserted Ultana.

ten minutes

dix minutes

deich nóiméad

Suddenly, a great big red fire engine, with blue lights flashing, zoomed past the garage window.

red

rouge

dearg

fire engine

camion de pompiers

inneall dóiteáin

It sped near to the shed and came to a screeching halt. Firefighters jumped out. Happy to see them, I barked and wagged my tail with delight.

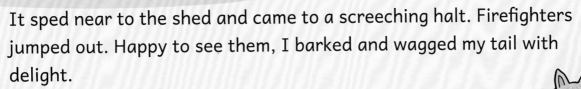

The red fire engine arrives at the shed.

Le camion de pompiers rouge arrive au hangar de la ferme.

Sroicheann an t-inneall dóiteáin dearg an tseid.

Finian shouted, "There's Georgia. I know her, and I'm glad she's in charge. She will quickly survey the scene. We will stay clear so that they can do their job safely."

What a sight met Georgia! Just as she walked towards the shed, there was a terrifyingly loud smash. Something shattered the shed door into smithereens and shot across the garden. Georgia ducked and yelled.

**What on earth was that?**

Both Ultana and Finian shuddered in shock. Yelping, I put my two front paws over my ears for a moment. Ultana roared over the noisy fire, "Georgia, it must have been the lawnmower blowing up."

"That makes sense", hollered Georgia.

lawnmower
tondeuse à gazon
lomaire faiche

BOOM!
BOOM!
BOOM!

Louder booming noises were heard coming from the shed. At the same time, I growled uncomfortably. "More objects must be exploding in the fire," Ultana exclaimed. Hurriedly, Georgia ran urgently towards Finian and Ultana.

Think very carefully and tell me what else is in the shed which could explode.

"I don't know. There are bicycles, tools, straw bales and turf piled high in the shed. Perhaps the noises are the lights exploding," bellowed Finian.

straw
paille
cochán

turf
tourbe
móin

"We are proceeding cautiously to keep the firefighters safe and will do our best to save the shed, but it could burn for a long time," explained Georgia as she spoke into her radio. "I need backup. Please send another fire engine."

A short time later a second engine drove rapidly to the scene.

"Start by directing your hoses at the roof and quickly try to dampen it down. It is NOT safe to go inside the shed or onto the roof," ordered Georgia.

| roof |
| toit |
| díon |

"How many litres of water will it take?" Ultana questioned Finian. "Lots. Luckily there is a hydrant nearby to refill the fire engine's drained water tank," Finian answered.

The fire engine requires a lot of water.

Le camion de pompiers utilise beaucoup d'eau.

Tá a lán uisce de dhíth ar an inneall dóiteáin.

Just then, the second fire engine took over promptly and continued to spray enormous amounts of water on the hot flames while the driver of the first machine drove off to the hydrant to refill.

smoke
fumée
deatach

Passers-by witnessed the enormous blaze and fog of smoke. Some visited to stare at the charred shed but the intense heat and burning smell prevented them from going close. Neighbours enquired if they could help but, until the firefighters had extinguished the fire, there was nothing that anyone else could do.

The flames are hot.
Les flammes sont chaudes.
Tá na lasracha an-te.

"Hello, I'm Doreen. Are you the shed owner?" a woman asked Finian. "Yes I am. I'm Finian," he responded.

"I work for the water company. Our computer system started to show a huge water loss from this hydrant. We were very puzzled, so I have driven out here and am glad to see there is no leak or burst pipe," admitted Doreen. "Hopefully the firefighters will save your shed. I'm away back to the office. Nice to meet you, Finian. Bye bye".

Meanwhile, I was absorbed watching all the action from the garage window and listening to the conversations taking place outside. Eventually, Ultana came to check on me.

"Good dog, Whiz Macgael. The fire is nearly out now," she whispered, as she carried me outside.

firefighter

sapeur-pompier

comhraiceoir tine

Moments later, a firefighter approached us and took off his big, yellow hat. "I'm Pierre. That's a nice, calm dog. Would you both like to view the fire engine?" quizzed Pierre while stroking my ears with his large gloves. I felt more at ease.

Yes, please.

Oui s'il vous plaît.

Ba mhaith, le do thoil.

ladder

échelle

dréimire

"Yes please," replied Ultana politely.

Just as the tank refilled, Pierre demonstrated the equipment, showing us the giant ladder on the roof, the fascinatingly long hose and all the apparatus at the front of the machine.

hose

lance à incendie

píopa uisce

"The flames are out. We just need to dampen a few smouldering turf to make sure the fire is doused completely and cannot relight. Some turf were taken outside to cool down. Unfortunately, they are soaking wet," uttered Pierre. "The shed and its roof are damaged and many contents destroyed, but we saved what we could. It has taken us about three hours."

The fire is out.

Le feu est éteint.

Tá an tine múchta.

three hours

trois heures

trí huaire

Naturally, I woofed with joy to hear that the fire was out.

"Thank you so much. You must be tired after your tough work. Would you like some tea, Pierre?" asked Ultana.

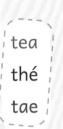

tea
thé
tae

Pierre laughed at his tummy grumbles. Ultana giggled. Chuckling, he joked that he would love something to eat as well, and called to the other firefighters to come into the house. Ultana rushed ahead into the kitchen and left me on my dog cushion in the corner. "Sit, Whiz Macgael. Stay there," fussed Ultana. As a well-trained pet, I did what Ultana asked.

By the time the kettle boiled, she had brought out a lovely tablecloth and set the table. Finian poured warm cups of tea for the exhausted firefighters. Hungry after their tiring work, the firefighters quickly ate all the tasty food.

The firefighters eat lunch.

Les sapeurs-pompiers déjeunent.

Itheann na comhraiceoirí tine lón.

As might be expected, Finian and Ultana were grateful for the brave efforts to save the shed. Appreciating the gratitude, the firefighters recounted entertaining anecdotes about fires they had fought. Refreshed, they thanked Finian and Ultana as they left the kitchen.

**Please check the shed one last time before you pack up the equipment, to ensure the fire has not relit.**

Shortly after, the fatigued firefighters climbed slowly into the fire engines. Ultana and Finian waved goodbye. Putting up my paw, I waved goodbye too and wagged my tail as the firefighters left to drive back to the fire station.

paw
patte
lapa

"Thank you so much, Whiz Macgael, for barking this morning and alerting me to the fire. You are a star and an extraordinary, super dog," declared Ultana proudly, as she gave me an extra-special pat on the head.

Despite the consequences of the fire, on the positive side, I'm having a well-earned rest while chewing on my reward of a few dog treats.

The Fire Adventure

Star

Good luck.
Bonne chance.
Ádh mór ort.

Super Dog

27

# The Lake Adventure

**Water rescue and safety**

The Lake Adventure
L'aventure du lac
Eachtra cois Locha

Lifebuoy (also known as ringbuoy or life ring)

lifebuoy
bouée de sauvetage
baoi tarrthála

sun
soleil
an ghrian

yellow
jaune
buí

swim
nage
snámh

Hi!
Salut !
Haigh!

# Summer: Sunny Walks Swimming

summer
été
an samhradh

walk
promenade
siúlóid

Life-saving with me

One lovely sunny day in summer, as I lay in the garden enjoying the sunlight, I heard Ultana calling,

"Come on, Whiz Macgael. I am driving to the lakes for our afternoon walk. Off we go."

Racing to the car, I leapt into the big boot of her modern motor car.

car
voiture
carr

I travel to the lake by car.
Je vais au lac en voiture.
Téim go dtí an loch sa charr.

"Look out the window at the giant, green trees, Whiz Macgael," Ultana encouraged as she drove carefully along the winding country road.

Soon we arrived at a beautiful, scenic, peaceful lake.

green
vert
glas

tree
arbre
crann

blue
bleu
gorm

With few clouds in the clear blue sky, the lake looked so calm and tranquil.

sky
ciel
spéir

lake
lac
loch

The sun is shining. The sky is blue.

Le soleil brille. Le ciel est bleu.

Tá an ghrian ag soilsiú. Tá an spéir gorm.

Firstly, Ultana fastened my lead securely to prevent me from running away. Eager to be outside in the warm sunshine, I jumped enthusiastically from the boot. Walking along the lakeside path, sniffing heather and fresh green mossy plant scents, was delightful. My sense of smell is much keener than that of people.

nose
nez
srón

Most importantly, Ultana has taught me good manners. As we passed people on the trail, I remembered not to jump. Wagging my tail excitedly, I sat resting on my back paws, offered my front ones in good-natured friendship and hoped to get patted on my soft, furry head. Sometimes it was fun to roll on my golden coloured back for a tickly tummy rub.

## Golden rules:

1. Sit, do not jump.
2. No muddy or wet pawprints on people.
3. Wag my tail.

golden
dorée
órga

Lengthy, magical strolls in the countryside were a great way to meet other dogs. My favourite was Tuffles, an attractive black and white collie dog.

black
noir
dubh

white
blanc
bán

With two picturesque lakes to stroll around, a little jetty and a hut for canoes, this was an ideal place to ramble. As a very well-brought-up dog and being particular about my appearance, I love to keep myself clean.

> lifeguard
>
> maître-nageur
>
> garda tarrthála

Rushing to the lake to wash my paws, Ultana interrupted, insisting that it was unwise for me to swim in the deep lake as the water could be dangerous and there was no sign of a lifeguard.

On that bright, balmy day, birds soared into the sky, and the occasional aeroplane flew high overhead. As Ultana and I walked along the footpath, a man was rowing a boat on the lake while two children were swimming front crawl far away. I observed them having fun splashing joyfully in the water.

> A man rows a boat.
>
> Un homme rame dans le bateau.
>
> Rámhaíonn fear bád.

The man paddled his boat, effortlessly manoeuvring, making gentle ripples in the water. Unexpectedly, shouting and splashing disrupted the peaceful day. Immediately, Ultana spun around and looked in the direction of the noise.

"The girl must have swallowed some water. She is coughing, spluttering and struggling. Oh no! She has disappeared under the water," cried Ultana as she spotted what was happening from the lakeside. "Help! Help, Dad. Erin has gone under the water," shouted the boy. Immediately, the man in the boat started rowing, as fast as he could, towards the sinking child.

Erin goes under the water.
Erin va sous l'eau.
Téann Erin faoin uisce.

A stolen life buoy is a stolen life

Ultana reacted swiftly. Running to the hut, she lifted an orange and white circle with a rope attached to it from a red box.

At once, I raced behind Ultana, hot on her heels, as she sprinted around the lake carrying the ring with her to the place closest to Erin. My lead tangled and opened as I ran.

orange
orange
oráiste

lifebuoy
bouée de sauvetage
baoi tarrthála

"Move back from the edge. Sit here, Whiz Macgael. When lifesaving, we need to keep ourselves safe. I must throw this lifebuoy as close as possible to Erin," declared Ultana.

Just as she hurled the lifebuoy faraway, she released its rope and shouted, "Lifebuoy, lifebuoy, lifebuoy." The boy yelled, "What do I do with it?" Ultana roared, "Stay calm. My name is Ultana. Swim towards Erin. Lift her head out of the water and ask her to hold the lifebuoy."

Ultana throws the lifebuoy.
Ultana lance la bouée de sauvetage.
Caitheann Ultana an baoi tarrthála.

Quick as a flash, seeing my chance and, being an intelligent dog, I leapt into the lake to help save this little child. Nosediving into the water, at first I plummeted downwards and was submerged deep in the lake's dark murky depths. Once I succeeded in rising to the surface, I gasped for air.

Barking and splashing, I swiftly doggy-paddled my way towards the lifebuoy. Finally, I arrived and used my nose to push the lifebuoy towards where Erin had disappeared. Meanwhile, the boy swam and dived frantically, attempting to locate his lost sister.

"I've found her," the boy hollered. He raised Erin's head from the water and put on the lifebuoy to keep her afloat.

Erin's dad reached her. He lifted her into the boat and instantly made sure she was breathing. Then he checked to see if she was hurt. Erin coughed up some water and her dad looked very relieved.

Throwing the lifebuoy back into the water, Erin's dad called, "Cling on tight, Mack. Can you hold the dog as well? The boat is too small for us all."

Erin is breathing. She is ok now.

Erin respire. Elle va bien maintenant.

Tá Erin ag análú. Tá sí i gceart arís.

Erin's dad grabbed the lifebuoy rope and pulled Mack and me behind his boat all the way to the jetty. When we arrived, Ultana ensured that everyone safely climbed out of the water. With a mobile phone in her hand, she enquired anxiously, "Do you need me to phone the emergency services?"

Do you need the emergency services?

Avez-vous besoin des services d'urgence ?

An bhfuil na seirbhísí éigeandála de dhíth ort?

"No thanks. I have trained in first aid and life-saving. Erin is breathing fine and has no injuries," her father reassured Ultana.

first aid

premiers secours

garchabhair

life-saving

secourisme

tarrtháil

Soon after, Mack and Erin shook my paws, and Erin started talking and laughing. I was so happy to see her smile. Erin's dad said warmly to Ultana, "Thank you so much for throwing the lifebuoy. You were amazing. What do you call your dog?"

"That's Whiz Macgael, and I'm Ultana".

Thank you.

Merci.

Go raibh maith agat.

Patting me on the head, "What a remarkable dog!" he proclaimed. "Thank you, Whiz Macgael, for helping save Erin's life. You are a real hero."

I save Erin's life.

Je sauve la vie d'Erin.

Déanaim tarrtháil ar Erin.

I was so proud to be called a hero.

**Yes, Whiz Macgael was a very heroic dog today. Luckily there was a lifebuoy available. Sometimes they can be damaged or stolen.**

Ultana put the lifebuoy and rope back in the box beside the lake, and we set off towards the car. Waving goodbye to everyone Ultana drove home while I relaxed in the boot.

Goodbye.

Au revoir.

Slán leat.

After a bath to remove all the smelly lake water and sticky, squelchy mud, I shook myself vigorously outside to release all the water from my fur.

Next, Ultana brought me inside. I loved the feeling of the whooshing warm air of the hairdryer as it blew and puffed through my coat, drying me thoroughly.

As a treat for helping with the rescue, Ultana presented me with a delicious, fishy-tasting dog treat which I munched quickly. Realising my hunger she brought my dog dish, and I hastily scoffed all the remaining food. Holding my front paws in her hands, she looked into my eyes and praised me, "Congratulations, Whiz Macgael. You were a hero and the crème de la crème of talented dogs today. I am overjoyed that you helped rescue Erin from the lake."

eyes
yeux
súile

I am a hero.
Je suis un héros.
Is laoch mé.

What a genuinely unexpected adventure I had at the lake!

Indeed, as I climbed into my cosy kennel at the end of that warm summer day, I knew without a doubt that I would sleep well.

Goodnight.
Bonne nuit.
Oíche mhaith.

Help me regain my health

# The Vet Adventure

Visit the vet with me

The Vet Adventure

L'aventure chez le vétérinaire

Eachtra leis an Tréidlia

40

One rainy autumn day, as the leaves changed colour and drifted down from the trees, I woke up not feeling my usual self.

autumn

automne

an fómhar

My left ear and neck, in particular, were sore to touch with my paw, and I did not want to eat or drink. Ultana carried me into the house straightaway to take care of me and asked if I was OK.

house

maison

teach

Are you OK?

Ça va ?

An bhfuil tú go maith?

No you are not OK.

Non, tu ne vas pas bien.

Níl tú go maith.

sick

malade

tinn

She kept me warm by giving me a cosy cushion and soft dog blanket. I just felt like resting all day. Even though she is a very clever owner, Ultana did not understand doggy barks. That day, however, she sensed that I was not feeling well. Maybe it was the shock of the fire in the farm shed in spring or getting extremely wet at the lake in summer, but I felt sick that day.

Usually, I am happy, healthy, energetic and enjoy being outside, walking and running. In contrast, refusing food, lacking energy, lying down a lot and sleeping gave her some clues. Besides, I did not even bark or growl at the noisy racket when the bin emptied into the large bin lorry.

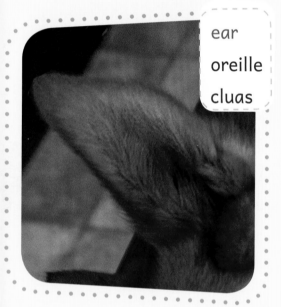

ear

oreille

cluas

Liquid oozed from my left ear, splashing onto the newly painted, cream wall as I whimpered, wriggled and shook my head trying to get out the gooey fluid. I worried that this would make

cream

couleur crème

dath an uachtair

Ultana cross with me but she is so kind that I did not need to be concerned. Instead, she was very attentive and keen to know what was wrong. As she cleaned my ear and felt my neck, I whined, giving a hint as to the problem. Ultana left me to make a telephone call.

I have a sore ear.

J'ai mal à l'oreille.

Tá cluas nimhneach orm.

Whiz Macgael, I have made an appointment and am taking you to the vet to look at your ear.

Lifting me carefully from my cushion, we then travelled into town by car. Arriving at the vets' surgery, the amiable, cheery receptionist greeted us, "Hello, I'm Cónán. What is the name of the ill little dog?"

"Whiz Macgael. I have an appointment for nine o'clock," replied Ultana.

It is nine o'clock.

Il est neuf heures.

Tá sé a naoi a chlog.

The appointment for Whiz Macgael is at nine o'clock.

Le rendez-vous de Whiz Macgael est à neuf heures.

Tá coinne ag Whiz Macgael ar a naoi a chlog.

Shortly afterwards, Alana, the vet, brought me into the treatment room. Ultana explained what was wrong including how my ear was oozing and asked the vet if she could check my teeth also. Alana examined me.

vet

vétérinaire

tréidlia

"It looks like Whiz Macgael might have an ear infection. I need to look inside her ear canal in case her eardrum has burst, but it is probably too sore today," advised Alana. As she peeked into my ear, I yelped in pain.

teeth
dents
fiacla

"I need to clean out her ears and scrub her teeth. These procedures require gas so that she will be in a deep sleep. Later in the week would suit best. Book an appointment to have both done on the same day. In the meantime, give her these tablets for the inner-ear infection and make sure she drinks plenty of fluids as her temperature is high," Alana explained.

I have a temperature.
J'ai de la fièvre.
Tá fiabhras orm.

Back at home, I just could not eat or drink anything. Ultana experimented with all sorts of liquids to try and help:

**1st:** **Chicken stock** - I coughed and made all kinds of funny noises, so she guessed that I did not like it, although I usually like chicken;

**2nd:** **Water** - this did not taste nice, so I refused;

**3rd:** **Raw vegetables** - a mixture of vegetables was taken out of the fridge and put through a juicing machine, coming out of the device as a liquid! The 'blended brew' was poured into a syringe and squirted into my mouth. The unique concoction tasted pleasant, and I drank it. Gradually, I started to recover and felt like eating.

# Cheers!

Good health!

Santé !

Sláinte!

I drink vegetable juice.

Je bois du jus de légumes.

Ólaim sú glasraí.

Ultana, therefore, tested me with various foods. Curries were my favourite and the reason my appetite started to improve as well as my desire for liquids.

She investigated how to get me to take the tablets, prescribed by the vet. I could not swallow them whole, so once crushed, she mixed the powder with some dog nuts and left them on a saucer, but I would not eat. Ultana tried them in my dinner, but they spoiled my delicious curry. In the end, I took the medication, separately from food, by licking the mixture off a big spoon!

Just then, Finian walked through the open door. He thought it was chocolate on the saucer and he nearly ate my dog nuts and tablets!

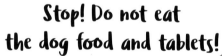

**Stop! Do not eat the dog food and tablets!**

Fortunately, Finian stopped just in time!

I lick the tablets from a spoon.

Je lèche les comprimés dans une cuillère.

Lím táibhléid ó spúnóg.

A few days later, Ultana took me to the vets' clinic. Although, I knew I was going to be given gas I did not know what to expect. Ultana patted my head gently before waving goodbye. Shortly afterwards, the vet carried me to a large table placing a snug blanket around me and a mask over my nose and mouth. I felt very, very sleepy as the gas started to take effect.

I visit the vet.

Je vais chez le vétérinaire.

Tugaim cuairt ar an tréidlia.

When I woke up, I was a bit scared but very reassured when Ultana arrived to take me home. Alana explained what happened when I was given gas, "George, my colleague, and I brushed Whiz Macgael's teeth, extracted a loose one, checked her ears and cleaned them carefully. Her eardrum is perfect."

Since Ultana was delighted that the procedures went so well she thanked the vets, Alana and George. Then she paid Cónán for my treatment. As a result of the gas, my head still felt fuzzy, and my paws were shaky and wobbly, so Ultana had to help me into and out of the car boot. Eventually, after a few unsteady days, I recovered fully. Adjusting to eating without one of my teeth, which I missed, took time.

As expected, Ultana looked after me very well, giving me a little more food each day. Since I no longer had a temperature, I could go on walks again. My health was restored. Soon my ear and neck were totally better, and I finally felt full of life again.

Thankfully, I was active and lively, happy to be outside and back in the garden in my usual daily routine. Ultana was so pleased to see me in good health again, and I aim to remain, in a word, healthy!

I am healthy.

Je suis en bonne santé.

Tá mé folláin.

Affectionate
Brave
Charming
Dog 🐾

Bye!
Salut !
Slán!

Thank you so much for reading about my adventures.
I hope that you enjoyed my heroic escapades!
Goodbye! Cheerio!

## Love, Whiz Macgael.

# Words translated into French and Irish

These language boxes are all in the present tense.

**French**

Nouns in French can be masculine or feminine. The abbreviation (m) means masculine so use un or le. a dog - un chien | the dog - le chien

| English |
| Français (French) |
| Gaeilge (Irish) |

The abbreviation (f) means feminine so use une or la.
a paw - une patte | the paw - la patte

## Colours

If you know that a person or animal is female use une or la or male use un or le. Whiz Macgael is a female dog so une chienne is used in this book.

| black | blue | brown |
| noir | bleu | marron |
| dubh | gorm | donn |

| cream | golden |
| couleur crème | dorée |
| dath an uachtair | órga |

For plural nouns change le or la to les and add an s to the noun unless it ends with s, x or z in which case there is no change. If the noun ends in eau or eu add an x to the end.
the dogs - les chiens | the paws - les pattes

| green | orange |
| vert | orange |
| glas | oráiste |

**Irish** – The Irish aims to comply with the current official standard for writing in the Irish language called An Caighdeán Oifigiúil.

| red | white | yellow |
| rouge | blanc | jaune |
| dearg | bán | buí |

The Heroic Escapades of Whiz Macgael

Les escapades héroïques de Whiz Macgael

Na réimeanna cróga ó Whiz Macgael

dog

chienne (f)

madra

I am a dog.

Je suis une chienne.

Is madra mé.

My name is Whiz Macgael.

Je m'appelle Whiz Macgael.

Is mise Whiz Macgael.

I am eight years old.

J'ai huit ans.

Tá mé ocht mbliana d'aois.

garden

jardin (m)

gairdín

kennel

niche (f)

cró madra

I live in a dog kennel in the garden.

J'habite dans une niche dans le jardin.

Tá mé i mo chónaí i gcró madra sa ghairdín.

My address is:

Mon adresse est :

Mo sheoladh:

food

nourriture (f)

bia

water

eau (f)

uisce

I eat dog food and drink water.

Je mange de la nourriture pour chiens et je bois de l'eau.

Ithim bia madraí agus ólaim uisce.

I exercise daily.

Je fais de l'exercice tous les jours.

Déanaim aclaíocht gach lá.

ear
oreille (f)
cluas

two ears
deux oreilles
dhá chluas

eye
oeil (m)
súil

eyes
yeux
súile

nose
nez (m)
srón

paw
patte (f)
lapa

paws
pattes
lapaí

four paws
quatre pattes
ceithre lapa

teeth
dents
fiacla

tail
queue (f)
eireaball

I bark and wag my tail.

J'aboie et je remue la queue.

Bím ag tafann agus croithim m'eireaball.

# Farm and shed

cow
vache (f)
bó

roof
toit (m)
díon

shed
hangar (m)
seid

straw
paille (f)
cochán

tractor
tracteur (m)
tarracóir

turf
tourbe (f)
móin

# Good manners and greetings

Welcome.
Bienvenue.
Fáilte.

Hello.
Bonjour.
Dia duit.

Hi!
Salut !
Haigh!

Bye!
Salut !
Slán!

Goodbye.
Au revoir.
Slán leat.

Love
Amitiés
Le grá

Yes, please.
Oui, s'il vous plaît.
Ba mhaith, le do thoil.

Thank you.
Merci.
Go raibh maith agat.

Are you OK?
Ça va ?
An bhfuil tú go maith?

Good health!
Santé !
Sláinte!

Good luck.
Bonne chance.
Ádh mór ort.

Goodnight.
Bonne nuit.
Oíche mhaith.

# Fire

The Fire Adventure

L'aventure du feu

Eachtra an Dóiteáin

---

Fire!

Au feu !

Tine!

---

The farm shed is on fire.

Le hangar de la ferme est en feu.

Tá an tseid feirme trí thine.

---

burning

en flammes

ag dó

---

Ultana telephones the emergency services.

Ultana téléphone aux services d'urgence.

Cuireann Ultana fios ar na seirbhísí éigeandála.

---

fire blanket

couverture anti-feu

pluid dóiteáin

---

Finian runs to the shed.

Finian court vers le hangar de la ferme.

Ritheann Finian go dtí an tseid.

---

fire extinguisher

extincteur (m)

múchtóir dóiteáin

---

firefighter

sapeur-pompier (m)

comhraiceoir tine

---

fire engine

camion de pompiers (m)

inneall dóiteáin

---

The red fire engine arrives at the shed.

Le camion de pompiers rouge arrive au hangar de la ferme.

Sroicheann an t-inneall dóiteáin dearg an tseid.

---

flames

flammes

lasracha

---

The flames are hot.

Les flammes sont chaudes.

Tá na lasracha an-te.

In the event of a fire:

Get out! Stay out and away from the fire! Call the Fire Service.

En cas d'incendie:

Sortez! Restez dehors et loin de l'incendie! Appelez les pompiers.

I gcás dóiteáin:

Téigh amach! Fan amuigh ón tine! Cuir fios ar an mbriogáid dóiteáin.

hose
lance à incendie (f)
píopa uisce

ladder
échelle (f)
dréimire

rescue
secours
tarrtháil

smoke
fumée (f)
deatach

smoke alarm
détecteur de fumée (m)
aláram deataigh

water
eau (f)
uisce

The fire engine requires a lot of water.
Le camion de pompiers utilise beaucoup d'eau.
Tá a lán uisce de dhíth ar an inneall dóiteáin.

The fire is out.
Le feu est éteint.
Tá an tine múchta.

The firefighters eat lunch.
Les sapeurs-pompiers déjeunent.
Itheann na comhraiceoirí tine lón.

# House and garden

car
voiture (f)
carr

garden
jardin (m)
gairdín

house
maison (f)
teach

lawn
pelouse (f)
faiche

lawnmower
tondeuse à gazon (f)
lomaire faiche

slide
toboggan (m)
sleamhnán

tea
thé (m)
tae

trampoline
trampoline (m)
trampailín

tree
arbre (m)
crann

# Lake

The Lake Adventure
L'aventure du lac
Eachtra cois Locha

lake
lac (m)
loch

I travel to the lake by car.
Je vais au lac en voiture.
Téim go dtí an loch sa charr.

boat
bateau (m)
bád

A man rows a boat.
Un homme rame dans le bateau.
Rámhaíonn fear bád.

lifebuoy
bouée de sauvetage (f)
baoi tarrthála

Ultana throws the lifebuoy.
Ultana lance la bouée de sauvetage.
Caitheann Ultana an baoi tarrthála.

lifeguard
maître-nageur
garda tarrthála

Erin goes under the water.
Erin va sous l'eau.
Téann Erin faoin uisce.

life-saving

secourisme

tarrtháil

---

Do you need the emergency services?

Avez-vous besoin des services d'urgence ?

An bhfuil na seirbhísí éigeandála de dhíth ort?

---

Erin is breathing. She is ok now.

Erin respire. Elle va bien maintenant.

Tá Erin ag análú. Tá sí i gceart arís.

---

swim

nage (f)

snámh

---

walk

promenade (f)

siúlóid

---

first aid

premiers secours

garchabhair

---

I am a hero.

Je suis un héros.

Is laoch mé.

---

I save Erin's life.

Je sauve la vie d'Erin.

Déanaim tarrtháil ar Erin.

## Numbers

| Number | English | French | Irish |
|--------|---------|--------|-------|
| 0 | zero | zéro | náid |
| 1 | one | un | a haon |
| 2 | two | deux | a dó |
| 3 | three | trois | a trí |
| 4 | four | quatre | a ceathair |
| 5 | five | cinq | a cúig |
| 6 | six | six | a sé |
| 7 | seven | sept | a seacht |
| 8 | eight | huit | a hocht |
| 9 | nine | neuf | a naoi |
| 10 | ten | dix | a deich |

one nose

un nez (m)

srón amháin

two ears

deux oreilles

dhá chluas

three hours

trois heures

trí huaire

four paws

quatre pattes

ceithre lapa

I am eight years old.

J'ai huit ans.

Tá mé ocht mbliana d'aois.

It is nine o'clock.

Il est neuf heures.

Tá sé a naoi a chlog.

ten minutes

dix minutes

deich nóiméad

## Seasons

| English | French | Irish |
|---------|--------|-------|
| spring | printemps | an t-earrach |
| summer | été | an samhradh |
| autumn | automne | an fómhar |
| winter | hiver | an geimhreadh |

## Vet

vet

vétérinaire (m)

tréidlia

The Vet Adventure

L'aventure chez le vétérinaire

Eachtra leis an Tréidlia

ear

oreille (f)

cluas

I have a sore ear.

J'ai mal à l'oreille.

Tá cluas nimhneach orm.

No you are not OK.

Non, tu ne vas pas bien.

Níl tú go maith.

teeth

dents

fiacla

I have a temperature.

J'ai de la fièvre.

Tá fiabhras orm.

I visit the vet.

Je vais chez le vétérinaire.

Tugaim cuairt ar an tréidlia.

The appointment for Whiz Macgael is at nine o'clock.

Le rendez-vous de Whiz Macgael est à neuf heures.

Tá coinne ag Whiz Macgael ar a naoi a chlog.

sick

malade

tinn

spoon

cuillère (f)

spúnóg

tablets

comprimés

táibhléid

I lick the tablets from a spoon.

Je lèche les comprimés dans une cuillère.

Lím táibhléid ó spúnóg.

I drink vegetable juice.

Je bois du jus de légumes.

Ólaim sú glasraí.

I am healthy.

Je suis en bonne santé.

Tá mé folláin.

# Weather

sky

ciel (m)

spéir

sun

soleil (m)

an ghrian

The sun is shining. The sky is blue.

Le soleil brille. Le ciel est bleu.

Tá an ghrian ag soilsiú. Tá an spéir gorm.

# My emergency skills

An emergency is:

- - - - - - - - - - - - - - - - - - - - - - - - - - - - - - - - - - - - - - -

The emergency services include:

- - - - - - - - - - - - - - - - - - - - - - - - - - - - - - - - - - - - - - -

- - - - - - - - - - - - - - - - - - - - - - - - - - - - - - - - - - - - - - -

If I need an emergency service I will telephone: - - - - - - - - - -

I know to call an emergency service when:

- - - - - - - - - - - - - - - - - - - - - - - - - - - - - - - - - - - - - - -

- - - - - - - - - - - - - - - - - - - - - - - - - - - - - - - - - - - - - - -

I called an emergency service when:

- - - - - - - - - - - - - - - - - - - - - - - - - - - - - - - - - - - - - - -

- - - - - - - - - - - - - - - - - - - - - - - - - - - - - - - - - - - - - - -

112 – Europe & India
999 – UK & Ireland
000 – Australia
911 – Canada & USA
119 – China & Japan
111 – New Zealand

# My swimming skills

I can swim _____ metres.

I swim:    Backstroke     Butterfly     Breaststroke

Freestyle     Sidestroke    _____

I have the following awards for swimming:

_____

_____

I have the following awards for life-saving and water safety:

_____

_____

I have studied the following first aid course:

_____

_____

# My pet

My pet is called: _____

My pet is a: _____

My pet lives: _____

My pet eats: _____

My pet sleeps: _____

Here is a picture of my pet!

# The meaning of my name

**Whiz** - a bright spark

**Mac** - son of
(even though I am a female dog!)

**Gael** - a person from France (Brittany),
Ireland or the Scottish Highlands
or a person who speaks a Gaelic language,
or it could mean 'hero' and 'strength'.

# Whiz Macgael

'a bright spark of a strong hero'.
(The definition I like!)

Grá Ultana Ltd
Grá Ultana Ltd aims to publish high-quality books.

Bye!
Salut !
Slán!

Ultana

Whiz Macgael